World Regional Geography Mapping Workbook

W. H. Freeman and Company

Publisher: Steven Rigolosi
Marketing Director: John Britch
Supplements Editor: Stephanie Ellis
Illustrations: Maps.com

ISBN 1-4641-2202-4

W.H. Freeman and Company
41 Madison Avenue
New York, NY 10010
Houndmills, Basingstoke RG21 6XS, England
www.whfreeman.com/geography

Printed in the United States of America.

First printing.

Table of Contents

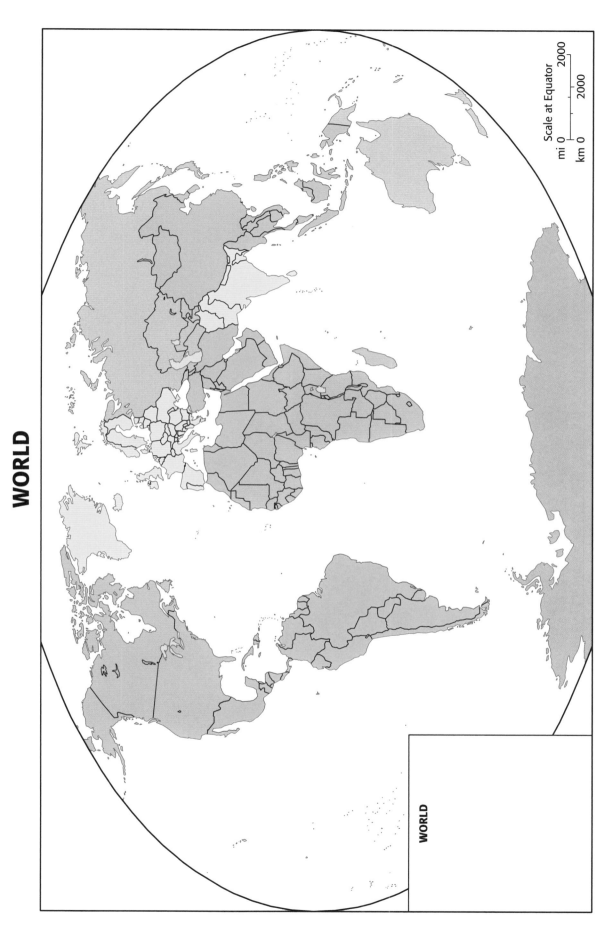

WORLD

Scale at Equator

mi 0   2000
km 0   2000

WORLD

NORTH AMERICA: Physical

NORTH AMERICA

mi 0   250   500
km 0 250 500

9

MIDDLE AND SOUTH AMERICA: Political

Caribbean Area

Anguilla (U.K.)
Antigua & Barbuda
Argentina
Aruba (Netherlands)
Bahamas
Barbados
Belize
Bolivia
Bonaire (Netherlands)
Brazil
British Virgin Islands (U.K.)
Chile

Colombia
Costa Rica
Cuba
Curaçao (Netherlands)
Dominica
Dominican Republic
Ecuador
El Salvador
Falkland Islands (U.K.)
French Guiana (France)
Galápagos Islands (Ecuador)
Grenada

Guadeloupe (France)
Guatemala
Guyana
Haiti
Honduras
Jamaica
Martinique (France)
Mexico
Montserrat (U.K.)
Nicaragua
Panama
Paraguay

Peru
Puerto Rico (U.S.)
St. Kitts & Nevis
St. Lucia
St. Martin
St. Vincent and the Grenadines
Suriname
Trinidad & Tobago
Uruguay
Venezuela
Virgin Islands (U.S.)

MIDDLE AND SOUTH AMERICA: Physical

MIDDLE & SOUTH AMERICA

mi 0   500   1000
km 0   800   1600

EUROPE: Political

Albania	Croatia	France	Kosovo	Netherlands	Sicily (Italy)
Austria	Cyprus	Germany	Latvia	Norway	Slovakia
Belgium	Czech Republic	Greece	Liechtenstein	Poland	Slovenia
Bosnia &	Denmark	Greenland	Lithuania	Portugal	Spain
Herzegovina	Estonia	(Denmark)	Luxembourg	Republic of Ireland	Sweden
Bulgaria	Faroe Islands	Hungary	Macedonia	Romania	Switzerland
Corsica (France)	(Denmark)	Iceland	Malta	Sardinia (Italy)	United Kingdom
Crete (Greece)	Finland	Italy	Montenegro	Serbia	

EUROPE: Physical

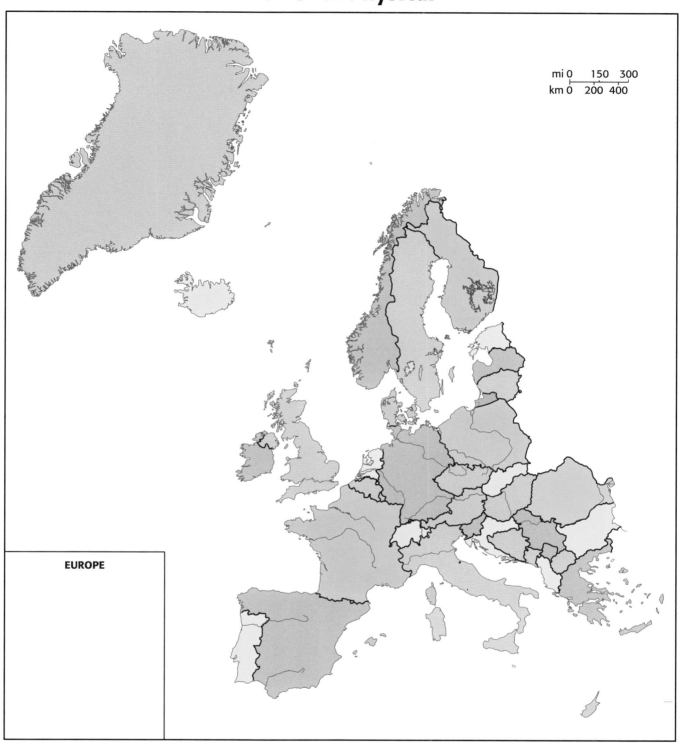

EUROPE

mi 0   150   300
km 0   200 400

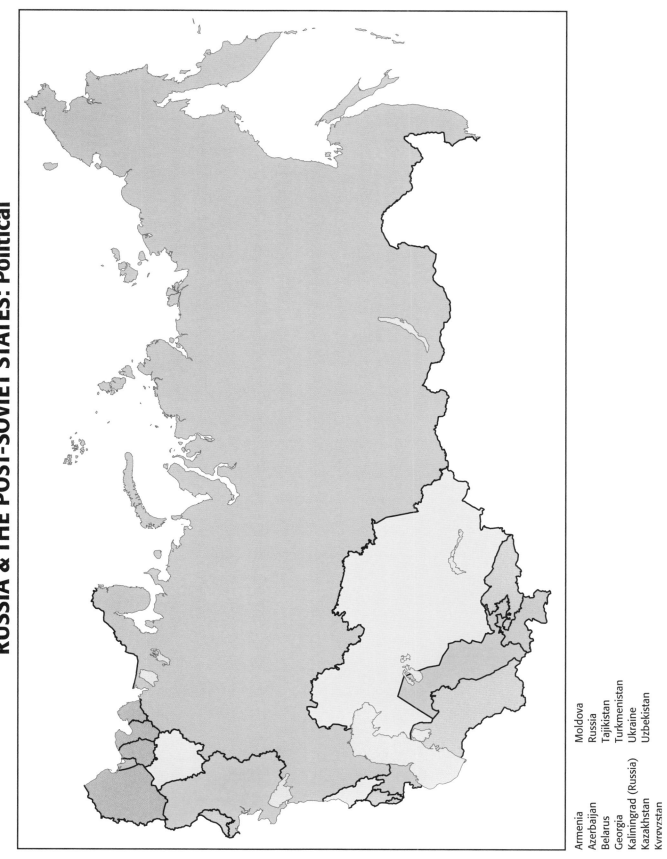

RUSSIA & THE POST-SOVIET STATES: Political

Armenia
Azerbaijan
Belarus
Georgia
Kaliningrad (Russia)
Kazakhstan
Kyrgyzstan

Moldova
Russia
Tajikistan
Turkmenistan
Ukraine
Uzbekistan

RUSSIA & THE POST-SOVIET STATES: Physical

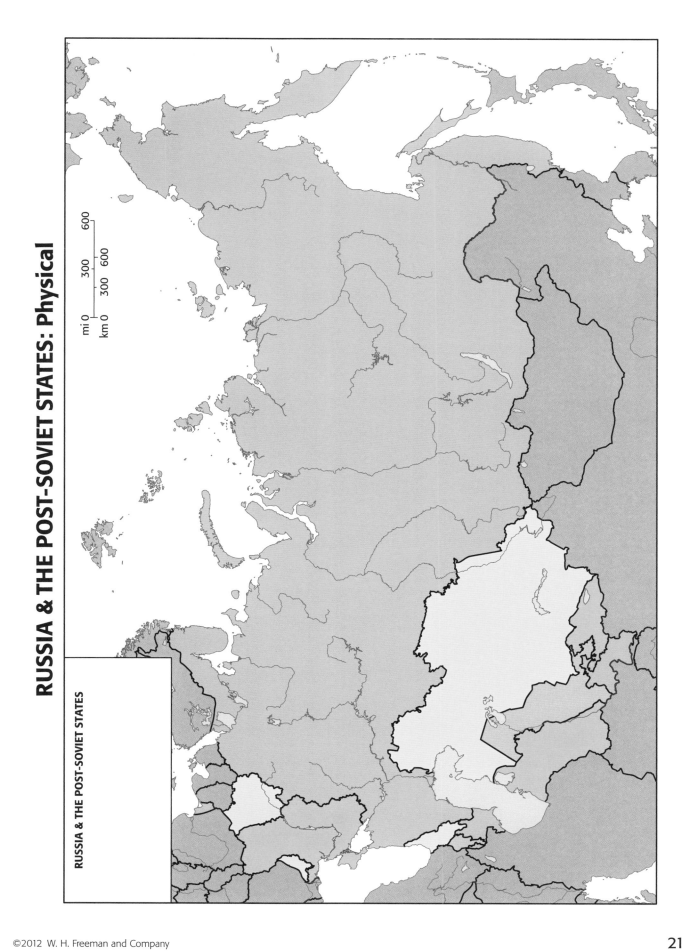

mi 0   300   600
km 0   300   600

RUSSIA & THE POST-SOVIET STATES

Algeria	Kuwait	Sudan	
Bahrain	Lebanon	Syria	
Egypt	Libya	Tunisia	
Iran	Morocco	Turkey	
Iraq	Oman	United Arab Emirates	
Israel	Qatar	Western Sahara (Morocco)	
Jordan	Saudi Arabia	Yemen	

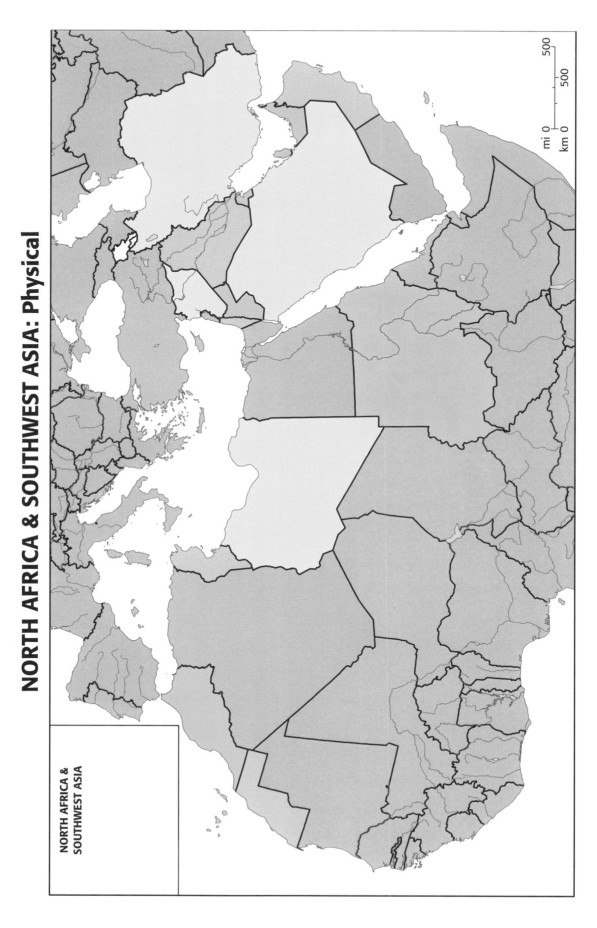

NORTH AFRICA & SOUTHWEST ASIA: Physical

NORTH AFRICA &
SOUTHWEST ASIA

mi 0   500
km 0   500

25

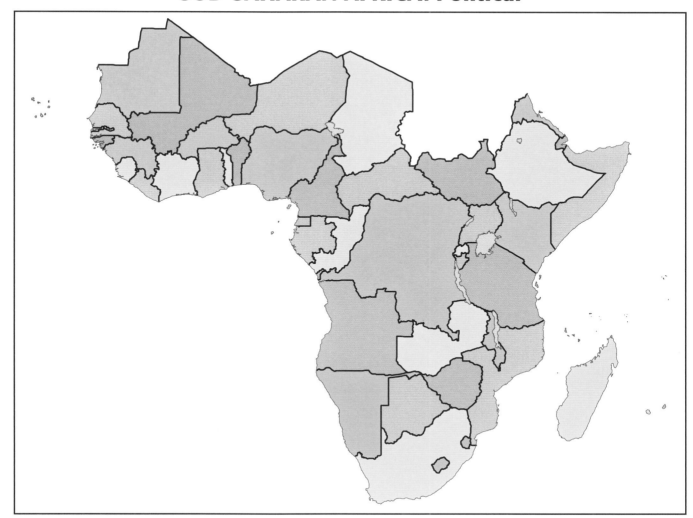

Angola	Ethiopia	Nigeria
Benin	Gabon	Republic of Congo
Botswana	(The) Gambia	Réunion (France)
Burkina Faso	Ghana	Rwanda
Burundi	Guinea	São Tomé & Príncipe
Cabinda (Angola)	Guinea-Bissau	Senegal
Cameroon	Kenya	Seychelles
Cape Verde	Lesotho	Sierra Leone
Central African Republic	Liberia	Somalia
Chad	Madagascar	South Africa
Comoros	Malawi	South Sudan
Côte D'Ivoire	Mali	Swaziland
Democratic Republic of the Congo	Mauritania	Tanzania
	Mauritus	Togo
Djibouti	Mozambique	Uganda
Equatorial Guinea	Namibia	Zambia
Eritrea	Niger	Zimbabwe

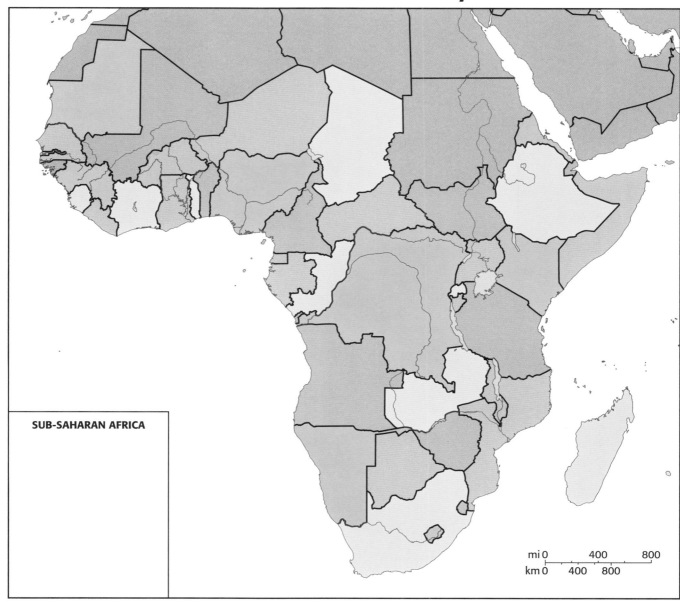

SUB-SAHARAN AFRICA

mi 0   400   800
km 0   400   800

Afghanistan
Andaman Islands (India)
Bangladesh
Bhutan
India
Laccadive Islands (India)
Maldives
Nepal
Nicobar Islands (India)
Pakistan
Sri Lanka

SOUTH ASIA: Physical

SOUTH ASIA

mi 0   200   400
km 0   200   400

EAST ASIA: Political

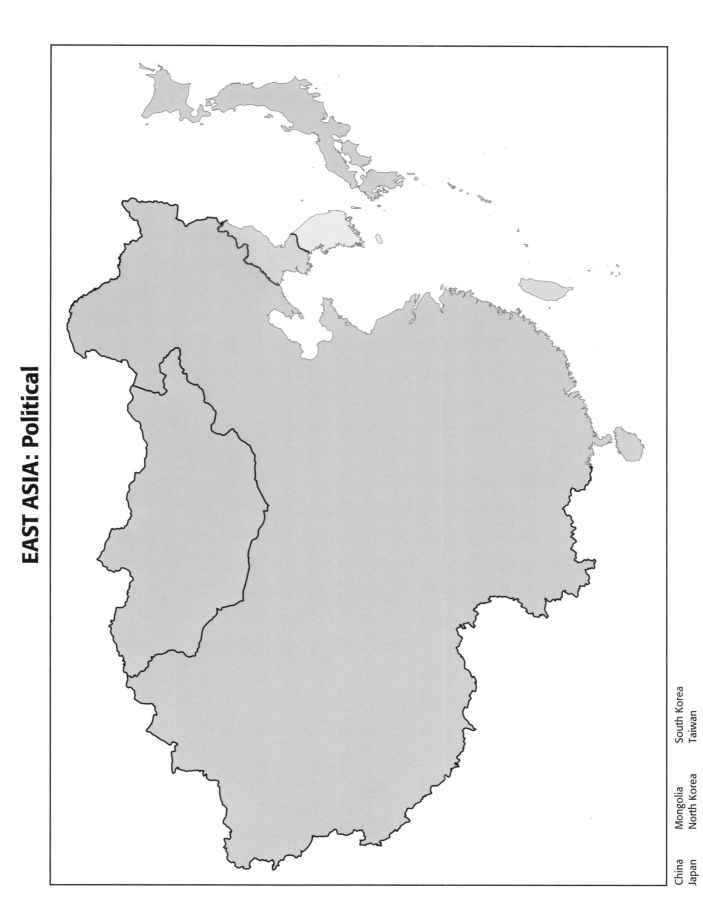

China
Japan

Mongolia
North Korea

South Korea
Taiwan

35

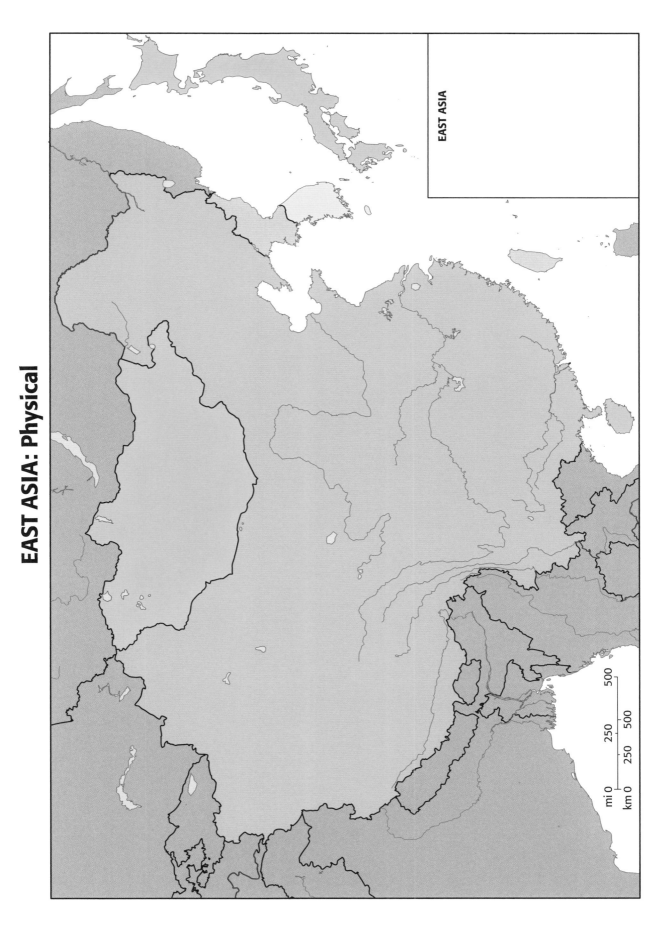

EAST ASIA: Physical

EAST ASIA

mi 0   250   500
km 0   250   500

CHINA/CHINESE PROVINCES

mi 0   250   500
km 0   250   500

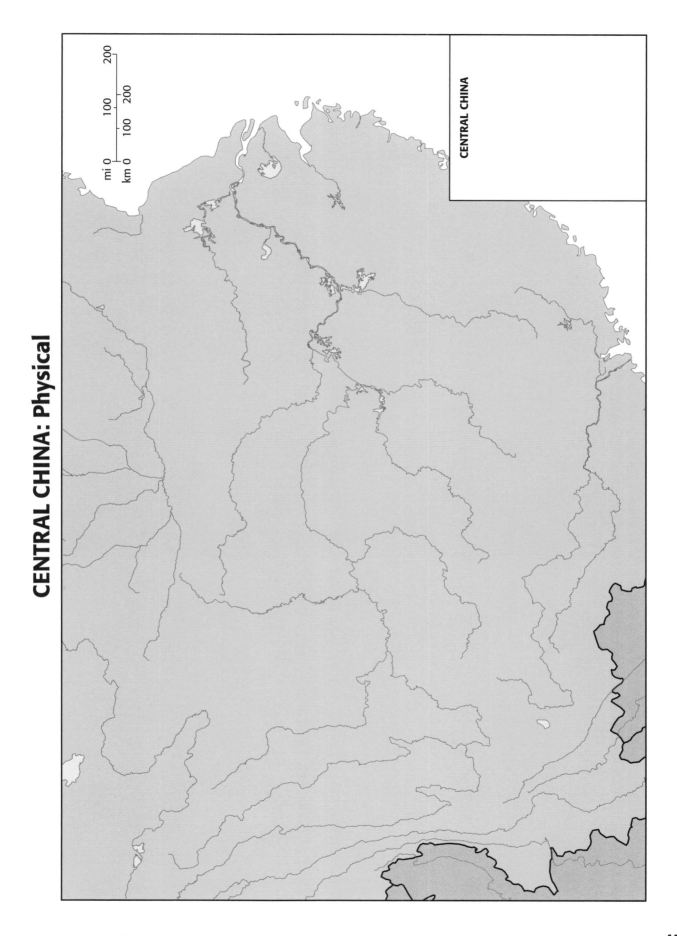

CENTRAL CHINA

mi 0
km 0
100
100
200
200

SOUTHEAST ASIA: Political

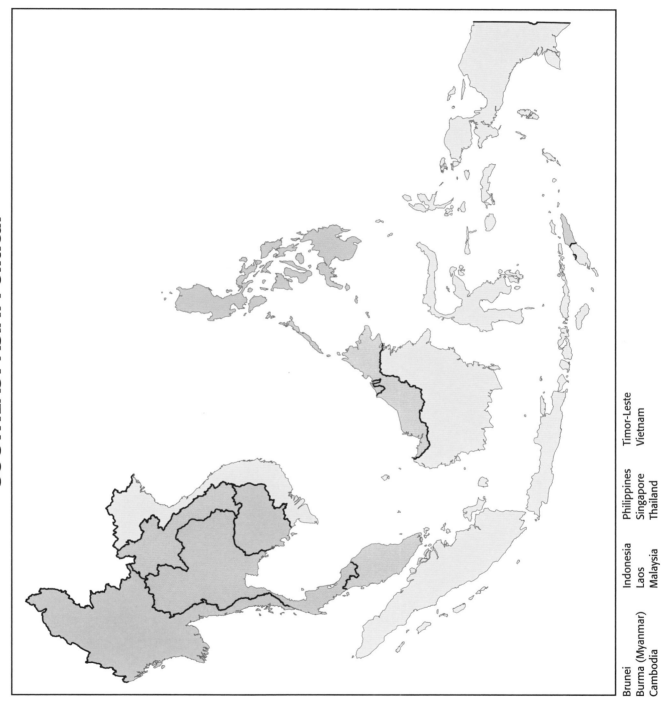

Brunei
Burma (Myanmar)
Cambodia

Indonesia
Laos
Malaysia

Philippines
Singapore
Thailand

Timor-Leste
Vietnam

SOUTHEAST ASIA: Physical

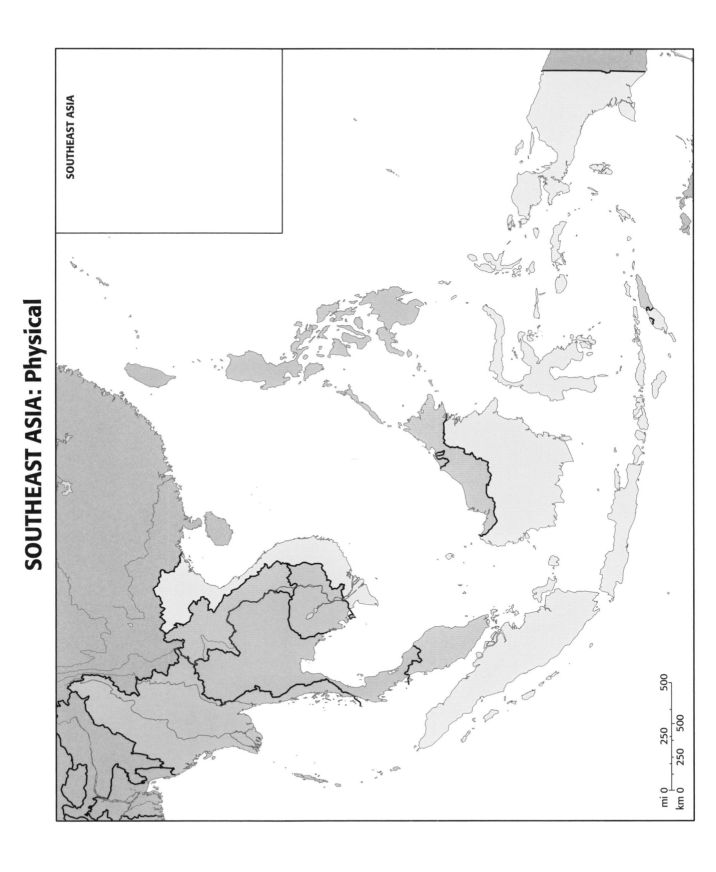

SOUTHEAST ASIA

mi 0   250   500
km 0   250   500

OCEANIA: Political

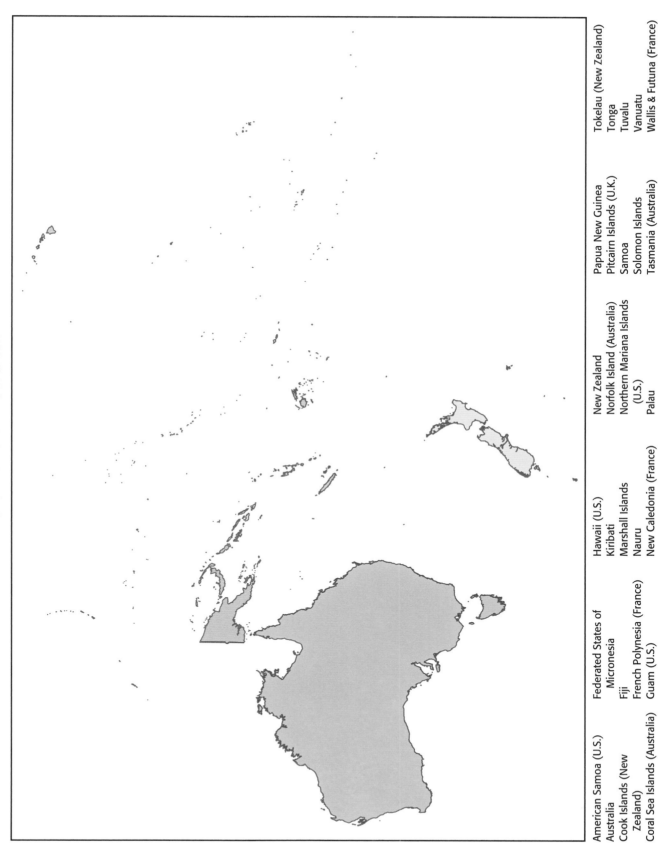

American Samoa (U.S.)
Australia
Cook Islands (New Zealand)
Coral Sea Islands (Australia)

Federated States of Micronesia
Fiji
French Polynesia (France)
Guam (U.S.)

Hawaii (U.S.)
Kiribati
Marshall Islands
Nauru
New Caledonia (France)

New Zealand
Norfolk Island (Australia)
Northern Mariana Islands (U.S.)
Palau

Papua New Guinea
Pitcairn Islands (U.K.)
Samoa
Solomon Islands
Tasmania (Australia)

Tokelau (New Zealand)
Tonga
Tuvalu
Vanuatu
Wallis & Futuna (France)

OCEANIA

mi 0   400   800
km 0   400   800